LIVE 8
SONGBOOK

This publication is not authorised for sale in
the United States of America and / or Canada

Wise Publications
part of The Music Sales Group

London / New York / Paris / Sydney / Copenhagen / Berlin / Madrid / Tokyo

Published by
Wise Publications
8/9 Frith Street, London, W1D 3JB, England.

Exclusive distributors:
Music Sales Limited
Distribution Centre, Newmarket Road,
Bury St Edmunds, Suffolk, IP33 3YB, England.

Music Sales Pty Limited
120 Rothschild Avenue, Rosebery, NSW 2018, Australia.

Order No. AM983466
ISBN 1-84609-186-1

This book © Copyright 2005 Wise Publications,
a division of Music Sales Limited.

Unauthorised reproduction of any part of this publication by
any means including photocopying is an infringement of copyright.

Compiled by Nick Crispin.
Cover photographs courtesy of LFI.

Printed at cost on a charitable basis by Caligraving Limited,
Thetford, Norfolk, Great Britain.

www.musicsales.com

LIVE 8

Before a worldwide TV audience estimated at three billion, Live8 entered history books on July 2 by becoming the most watched pop event ever. The charismatic Bob Geldof once again managed to harness the power of pop to put across his powerful message to world leaders: we, the people, demand that something be done about the perpetual crisis in Africa.

The inspiration for the event came from Bono and screenwriter Richard Curtis, and it wasn't until the U2 front man came up with the idea of opening the show with 'Sgt Pepper's Lonely Hearts Club Band', to be sung by Paul McCartney with the Dublin superstar quartet as his backing band, that Geldof was convinced of the viability of trying to top Live Aid. It wasn't exactly 'twenty years ago today' but near enough for Geldof to get on board, open his black book and begin recruiting.

So it was that at 2pm the former Beatle found himself singing the opening line of the opening song of what many consider to be the greatest album of all time – backed up by the biggest band in the world who promptly followed him, closing their set with 'One'. Normally, this would be the sort of extravaganza that would close any show and in any other circumstances Coldplay's Chris Martin would have been shaking in his trainers at the thought of following it, but the audience warmed to his obvious sincerity, especially when he inserted a few lines from 'Rockin' All Over The World' – the song with which Status Quo opened Live Aid – into 'In My Place'.

There followed a parade of superstars, the likes of which certainly hadn't been seen since Live Aid, among them Elton John, R.E.M., Annie Lennox, Madonna, Robbie Williams, The Who and Pink Floyd. Amid the many highlights was Geldof's own unplanned appearance with the inevitable 'I Don't Like Mondays', and Dido's pairing with Youssou N'Dour, the only African artist to appear. Madonna was characteristically ambitious, backed by the London Community Choir, while Robbie Williams, introduced by England football captain David Beckham, covered Queen's 'We Will Rock You' before singing 'Let Me Entertain You' and 'Angels'.

But the day didn't belong only to established superstars. After Keane and Razorlight, The Killers brought a touch of aggressive rock'n'roll mayhem to the stage, and were joined on guitar by Slash, the top-hatted guitar hero of Guns'n' Roses. The quirky Scissor Sisters performed a powerful, crowd-pleasing set while Joss Stone, whose soulful style belies her age, must have gained many new admirers.

For many, though, the highlight of the night was the penultimate act, Pink Floyd. Somehow Bob Geldof had managed to persuade the classic Floyd line-up of Rogers Waters, David Gilmour, Rick Wright and Nick Mason to set aside their differences for the sake of the cause, and following a spirited set by The Who, the audience was serenaded by this most ethereal of bands performing 'Breathe', 'Money', 'Wish You Were Here' and 'Comfortably Numb'. Bereft of their usual props and lights, Floyd's music seemed to take on an added warmth as the night drew in. The moving sight of this much loved British band together again was made all the more poignant when Waters dedicated 'Wish You Were Here' to Syd Barrett, their founding genius.

In the end it was left to Paul McCartney, nowadays rock's senior figure, to close out the day with a Beatles medley of 'Get Back', 'Drive My Car', on which he was joined by George Michael, 'Birthday' and 'The Long And Winding Road' which segued into the coda of 'Hey Jude', the ideal climactic sing-along.

Whether the world leaders who met at Gleneagles the following week got the message remains to be seen, but the day's events proved yet again the potency of our popular music as a unifying force in this divided world.

Sgt. Pepper's Lonely Hearts Club Band

Words & Music by John Lennon & Paul McCartney

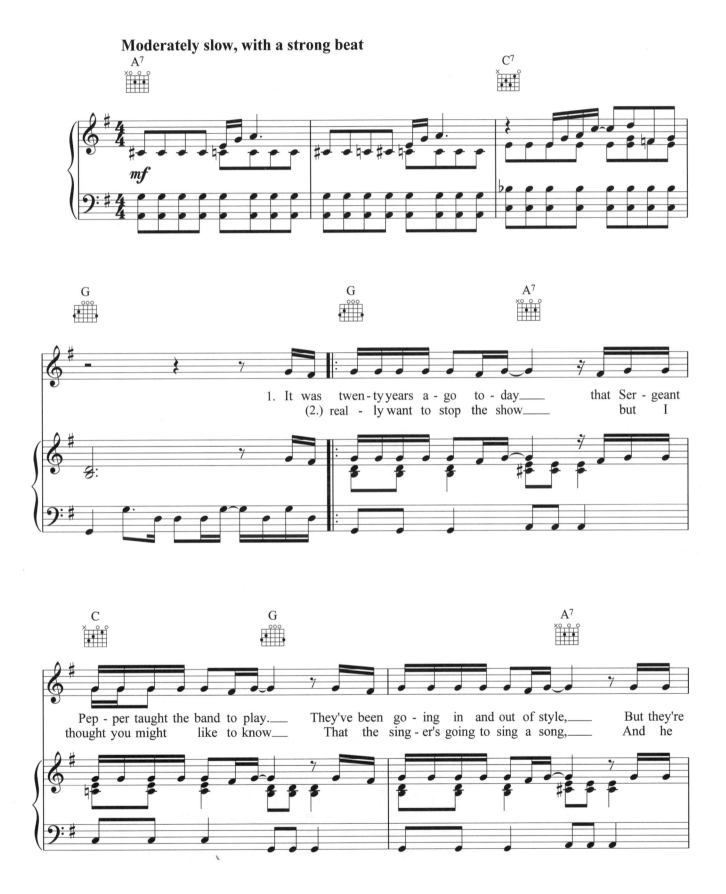

Moderately slow, with a strong beat

1. It was twen-ty years a-go to-day___ that Ser-geant
(2.) real-ly want to stop the show___ but I

Pep-per taught the band to play.___ They've been go-ing in and out of style,___ But they're
thought you might like to know___ That the sing-er's going to sing a song,___ And he

© Copyright 1967 Northern Songs.
All Rights Reserved. International Copyright Secured.

guar - an - teed to raise a smile.___ So may I in - tro - duce to you___ the
wants you all to sing a - long.___ So let me in - tro - duce to you___ the

act you've known for all these years;___
one and on - ly Bil - ly Shears.___

Ser - geant Pep - per's Lone - ly Hearts Club

Band.___

We're

won - der - ful to be here, It's cer - tain - ly a thrill, you're such a love - ly au - di - ence, we'd

like to take you home with us, we'd love to take you home. 2. I don't Ser - geant Pep - per's Lone - ly Hearts

Club Band.____ We'd like to thank you once a - gain.____

Ser - geant Pep - per's one and on - ly Lone - ly Hearts Club Band; It's

One

Words & Music by David Evans, Adam Clayton,
Paul Hewson & Laurence Mullen

1. Is it get - ting___ bet - ter___
2. Did I dis - ap - point you,
3. Have you come here___ for for - give - ness?

© Copyright 1991 Blue Mountain Music Limited/PolyGram International Music Publishing B.V/Mother Music Limited.
All Rights Reserved. International Copyright Secured.

Fix You

Words & Music by Guy Berryman, Chris Martin, Jon Buckland & Will Champion

1. When you try____ your best but you don't suc-ceed,____ when you get____ what you want but not what you need,____ when you feel____ so tired but you can't sleep,____

© Copyright 2005 BMG Music Publishing Limited.
All Rights Reserved. International Copyright Secured.

19

Lights will guide____ you home____ and ig - nite____ your bones____

____ and I will try____ to fix you.

3. And

Guitar

Saturday Night's Alright For Fighting

Words & Music by Elton John & Bernie Taupin

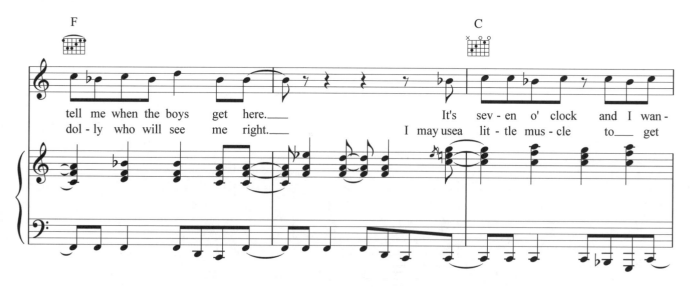

© Copyright 1973 Dick James Music Limited.
Universal/Dick James Music Limited.
All Rights Reserved. International Copyright Secured.

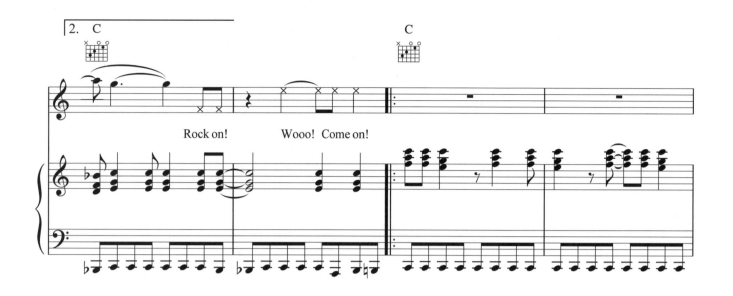

Rock on!   Wooo! Come on!

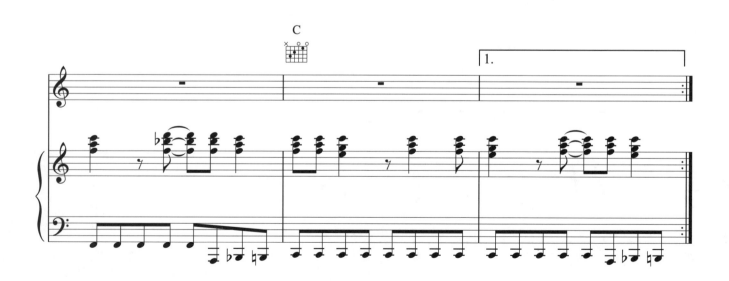

Seven Seconds

Words & Music by Cameron McVey, Jonathan Sharp,
Neneh Cherry & Youssou N'Dour

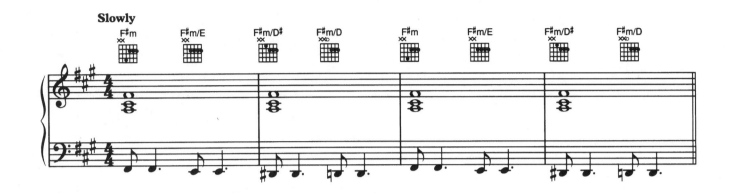

Bul ma seen bul ma djiss ma di re nga fook ni mann xa-mu-ma li nee ka thi

sa ma suul ak thi gui naw Ba-gu-ma ku ma xool daal di ne yaaw Li nee-ka thi yaaw mo

© Copyright 1994 EMI Virgin Music Limited (75%)/EMI Music Publishing Limited (25%).
All Rights Reserved. International Copyright Secured.

J'as- su - me les rai - sons___ qui nous poussent de chang - er tout.___

J'ai - me - rai qu'on ou - blie leur cou - leur, pour___ qu'ils es - per - ent.

Beau-coup de sen - ti-ments de race qui___ font qu'ils deses-pe - rent. (Je veux que les por-tes soient grande-ment ouv-ertes,

pour qu'ils puis-sent parl- er de leurs pei-nes, de leurs joies. Pour qu'on leur file des in-formations qui ne devisent pas) chan-ger.

sec - ond. Sev - en sec - onds a - way.___ Just as long as I stay,_____ I'll be wait

- ing. It's not a sec - ond. Sev - en sec - onds a - way. Just as long as I

stay,_____ I'll be wait - ing. It's not a

Everybody Hurts

Words & Music by Peter Buck, Bill Berry,
Mike Mills & Michael Stipe

© Copyright 1992 Night Garden Music/Uni-Chappell Music, USA.
Warner/Chappell Music Limited.
All Rights Reserved. International Copyright Secured.

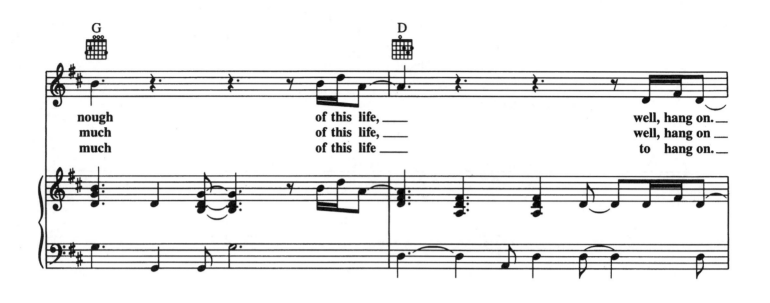

nough   of this life, ___   well, hang on. __
much   of this life, ___   well, hang on __
much   of this life ___   to   hang on. __

___   Don't let your - self   go,
___   'cause eve - ry - bod - y   hurts.
___   Well, eve - ry - bod - y   hurts   some-

         eve - ry - bod - y   cries
         Take com - fort __ in your friends.
times,   eve - ry - bod - y   cries.

41

Redemption Song

Words & Music by Bob Marley

Moderately, folk style

Old pi - rates, yes, they rob
pate your - selves from men - tal

I. Sold I to the mer - chant ships
slav - 'ry, none but our - selves can free our minds.

© Copyright 1980 Blue Mountain Music Limited/Fifty-Six Hope Road Music Limited/Odnil Music Limited.
Administered by Fairwood Music Limited.
All Rights Reserved. International Copyright Secured.

Em / C / D

a - tion___ tri - umph - ant - ly.
part of it. We've got to ful - fill the___ book.

G / C / D

Won't you help to sing___ these songs of

G / C / D / Em

free - dom? 'Cause all I ev - er had,___

C / D / G **To Coda** ⊕ / C / D

re - demp - tion___ songs, re - demp - tion

44

Somewhere Only We Know

Words & Music by Tim Rice-Oxley, Tom Chaplin & Richard Hughes

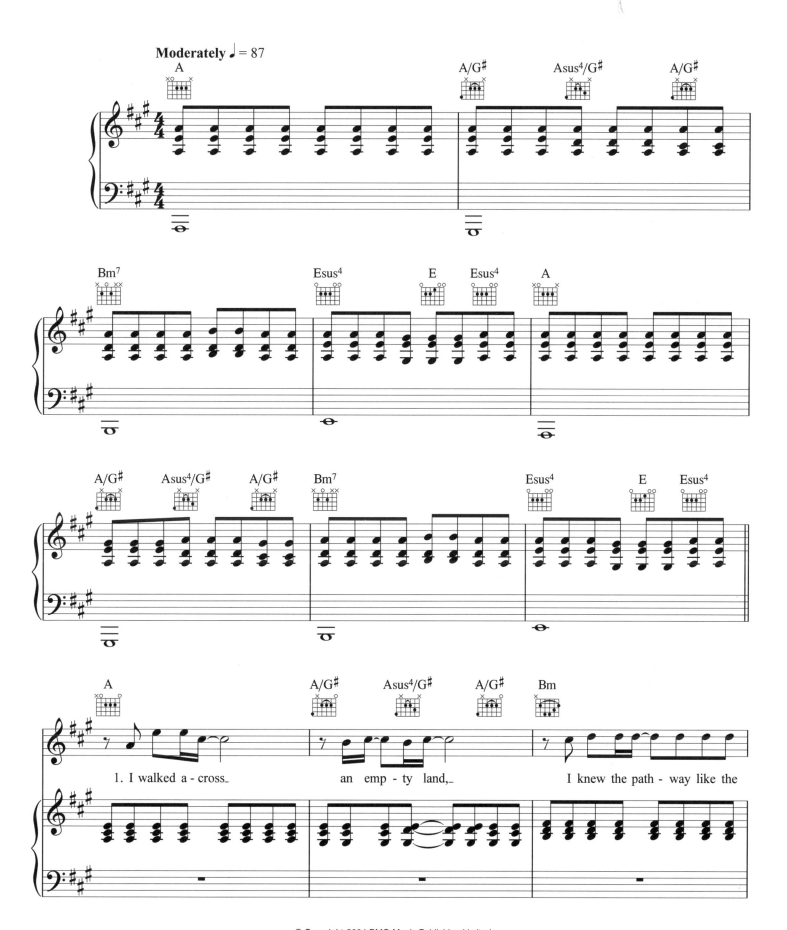

© Copyright 2004 BMG Music Publishing Limited.
All Rights Reserved. International Copyright Secured.

LET IT BE

COPYRIGHT © 1970 NORTHERN SONGS LIMITED
ALL RIGHTS ADMINISTERED BY BLACKWOOD MUSIC INC. UNDER LICENSE FROM ATV MUSIC (MACLEN)

I Don't Like Mondays

Words & Music by Bob Geldof

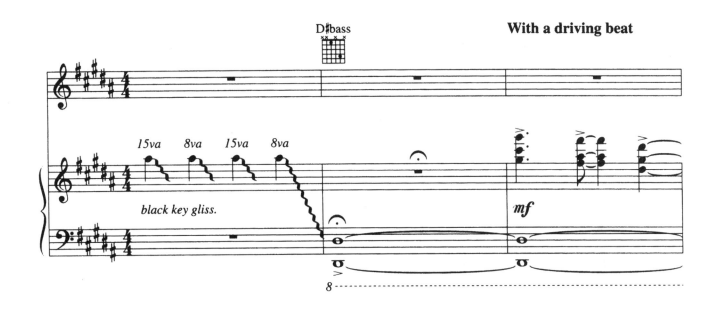

© Copyright 1979 Promostraat BV, Holland.
Sherlock Holmes Music Limited.
All Rights Reserved. International Copyright Secured.

55

56

down,   down,   down,   shoot it all down.___

And all the

58

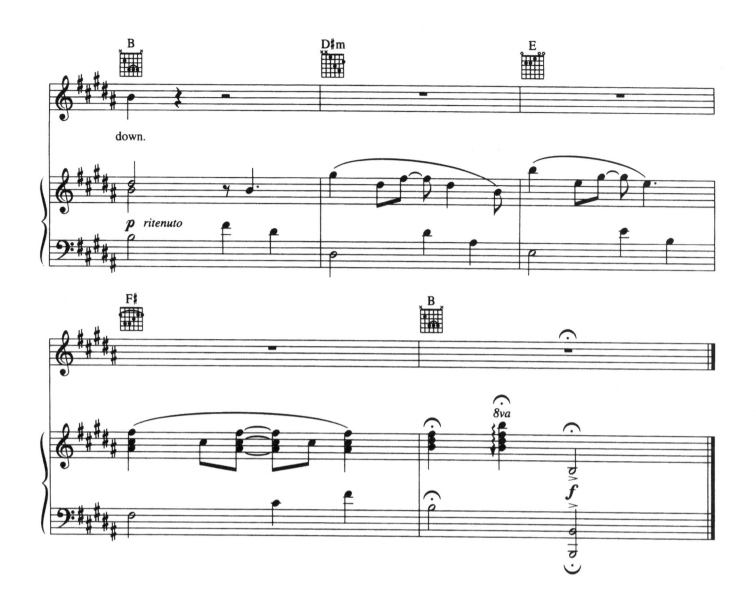

down.

Why

Words & Music by Annie Lennox

© Copyright 1992 La Lennoxa Limited.
BMG Music Publishing Limited.
All Rights Reserved. International Copyright Secured.

I tell my-self too ma-ny times, why don't you e-ver learn to keep your big mouth shut?____ That's why it hurts so bad to hear the words that keep on____ fall-ing from your mouth,____ fall-ing from_ your mouth, fall-ing from_ your mouth. Tell me

rubato

66

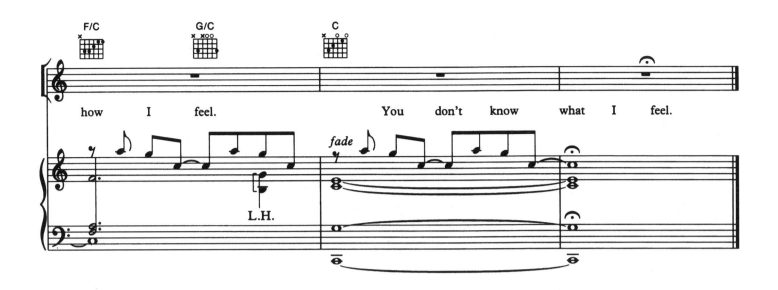

how I feel.   You don't know what I feel.

Verse 2

I may be mad, I may be blind,
I may be viciously unkind,
But I can still read what you're thinking.
And I've heard it said too many times
That you'd be better off,
Besides, why can't you see this boat is sinking?

Let's go down to the water's edge
And we can cast away those doubts,
Some things are better left unsaid,
But they still turn me inside out.
Turning inside out ... turning inside out.

Food For Thought

Words & Music by James Brown, Brian Travers, Robin Campbell, Norman Hassan,
Earl Falconer, Michael Virtue, Alistair Campbell & Terrence Wilson

© Copyright 1979 Graduate Music/New Claims Music Limited.
Complete Music Limited (25%)/Sanctuary Music Productions Limited (75%).
All Rights Reserved. International Copyright Secured.

Verse 2:
Skin and bones is creeping,
Doesn't know he's dead,
Ancient eyes are peeping
From his infant head.

Verse 3:
Politicians argue,
Sharpening their knives,
Drawing up their bargains,
Trading baby lies.

Verse 5:
Eat and drink rejoicing,
Joy is here to stay,
Jesus, son of Mary
Is born again today.

Somewhere Else

Song by Johnny Borrell
Music by Razorlight

© Copyright 2005 Sony/ATV Music Publishing (UK) Limited.
All Rights Reserved. International Copyright Secured.

74

Like A Prayer

Words & Music by Madonna & Pat Leonard

© Copyright 1989 EMI Music Publishing Limited (25%)/Sony/ATV Music Publishing (UK) Limited (25%)/Warner Chappell Music Limited (50%).
All Rights Reserved. International Copyright Secured.

Just like a dream _ you are not what you _ seem. _

_ Just like a prayer, _ no choice, your voice can take me

there. (Just like a prayer _ I'll _ take you there. _

No Chord

It's like a dream _ to me. _)

_)

84

85

Run

Words & Music by Gary Lightbody, Jonathan Quinn,
Mark McClelland, Nathan Connolly & Iain Archer

I sing it one last time for you,

© Copyright 2003 Big Life Music Limited (95%)/Copyright Control (5%).
All Rights Reserved. International Copyright Secured.

we don't have_____ time_____ for that,

all I want's to find an_____ eas - - ier way to

get out of our lit - tle____ heads.____

Have heart my dear, we're bound to_____ be____

af - raid, ev - en if it's just for a few days,

mak - ing up for all this mess.

Guitar solo

91

Light up, light up, as if you____ have____ a choice.

Ev - en if you can - not____ hear____ my voice,

I'll be right be - side you____ dear._

All These Things That I've Done

Words & Music by Brandon Flowers, Dave Keuning,
Mark Stoermer & Ronnie Vannucci

© Copyright 2004 Universal Music Publishing Limited.
All Rights Reserved. International Copyright Secured.

hold on,   if you can   hold   on,   hold on.

If you can___ hold___ on.___

If you can___ hold on.___

I Had A Dream

Words & Music by John B. Sebastian

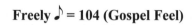

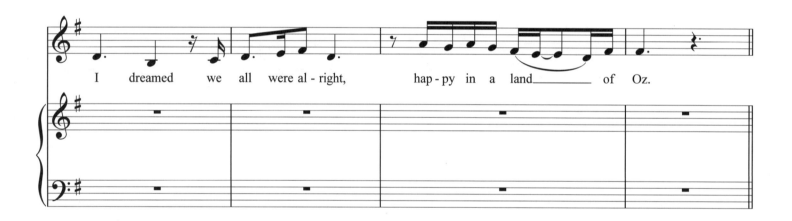

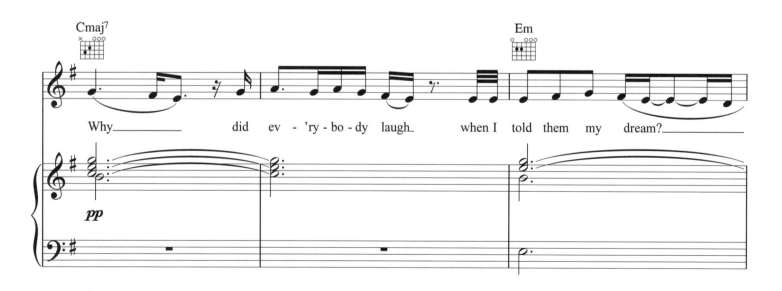

© Copyright 1968 Alley Music Corporation/Trio Music Company Incorporated, USA.
T.M. Music Limited (50%)/Windswept Music (London) Limited (50%).
All Rights Reserved. International Copyright Secured.

Message In A Bottle

Words & Music by Sting

© Copyright 1979 Magnetic Publishing Limited/EMI Music Publishing Limited.
All Rights Reserved. International Copyright Secured.

110

Angels

Words & Music by Robbie Williams & Guy Chambers

© Copyright 1997 EMI Virgin Music Limited (50%)/BMG Music Publishing Limited (50%).
All Rights Reserved. International Copyright Secured.

114

Won't Get Fooled Again

Words & Music by Pete Townshend

© Copyright 1971 Fabulous Music Limited.
All Rights Reserved. International Copyright Secured.

Wish You Were Here

Words & Music by David Gilmour & Roger Waters

© Copyright 1975 Pink Floyd Music Publishers Limited/Roger Waters Music Overseas Limited/Warner/Chappell Artemis Music Limited.
All Rights Reserved. International Copyright Secured.

120

rail____
What have we found_____ the same__ old__ fears____

a smile__ from a veil,____

Do you think you can tell____
Wish you__ were here____

And did they get you to trade

your he - roes for ghosts,

hot ash - es for trees,____

hot air__ for a cool__

breeze, cold comfort for charge

And did you exchange a walk on part in the war

for a lead role in a cage

Da da da da   da da da da da

124

The Long And Winding Road

Words & Music by John Lennon & Paul McCartney

© Copyright 1970 Northern Songs.
All Rights Reserved. International Copyright Secured.

123456789

Your Guarantee of Quality:
As publishers, we strive to produce every book
to the highest commercial standards.

The book has been carefully designed to minimise awkward page
turns and to make playing from it a real pleasure. Particular care has
been given to specifying acid-free, neutral-sized paper made from
pulps which have not been elemental chlorine bleached.

This pulp is from farmed sustainable forests and
was produced with special regard for the environment.

Throughout, the printing and binding have been planned
to ensure a sturdy, attractive publication which should give
years of enjoyment.

If your copy fails to meet our high standards, please inform us
and we will gladly replace it.